STO S

A CITY GUIDE

FOR THE

IMAGINATION

EDITED BY
ROSAMUND DAVIES   CHERRY POTTS   KAM REHAL

ARACHNE PRESS

First published in UK 2019 by ARACHNE PRESS Limited
100 Grierson Road, London SE23 1NX
www.arachnepress.com
© Arachne Press Limited

ISBNs:
print: 978-1-909208-78-0
ePub: 978-1-909208-79-7
mobi/kindle: 978-1-909208-80-3

Thanks to Muireann Grealy for her proofing.

Printed on wood-free paper in the UK by
TJ International, Padstow.

INDIVIDUAL COPYRIGHT

3

CONTENTS

CAFÉS

MAIN STREETS

MARKET

CROSSROADS

SIDE STREETS

SQUARES AND PARKS

INTRODUCTION

Which city are you in? How have you come to be here? What are the characters, voices, stories that you have come across in your city? Your experiences – the people and places you encounter, the things you hear and see, the thoughts and sensations you feel – are at once individual and also connected to countless others in cities everywhere. Your city is also *the city*.

These were the thoughts that inspired us to put together this collection. Through the voices and perspectives of many different writers, it offers readers a book that they can take with them into the city to experience it through stories.

You will not find in its pages any cities, landmarks, or even characters that are identified by name. These are stories about any city, every city in which you might find yourself. The story of the woman sitting in front of you on the bus, the waiter in your café, or even the spider on the pavement.

As you read them, maybe you will also start to see – in the streets and alleyways and cafés and hotels of this city, the one you are standing in now – the lines and traces of other cities: familiar cities, past cities, cities of the future, cities of the imagination.

We would like to invite you to share your experience of the city through your own photos. You can email them to us at *StoryCities@gre.ac.uk*, telling us if it relates to a particular story in the book. Or share them via instagram: *story_cities_book*, twitter: *@storycities #storycities* or Facebook: *https://www.facebook.com/StoryCities/*

Rosamund Davies & Kam Rehal

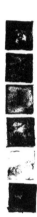

TERMINI

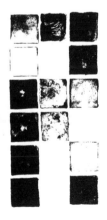

TODAY'S ARRIVALS AND DEPARTURES

Rosamund Davies

Those who have just arrived
Those who are going home
Those who have left home
Those who are on leave
Those who have left it all behind
Those who are on holiday
Those who are here on business
Those who work here
Those who need work
Those who need money
Those who are here for the season
Those who are lost
Those who have something to lose
Those who are fleeing a war
Those who are carrying a passport
Those who have a ticket
Those who have something to sell
Those who have something to give
Those who are homeless
Those who are travelling light
Those who packed the night before
Those who are thirsty

Those who are hungry
Those who have missed their train
Those who will not be missed
Those who are waiting for someone
Those who are waiting for a connection
Those who do not mind waiting
Those who check their watch repeatedly
Those who are in a hurry
Those who look straight ahead
Those who look around
Those who look down
Those whose feet hurt
Those who are looking for somewhere to sit
Those who are looking for somewhere to sleep
Those who have just woken up
Those who remember what it used to be like
Those who want to make a new start
Those who are returning
Those who are going to war
Those who come and go
Those who will never leave
Those who are leaving for good

FEET IN A YARD

Sarah-Clare Conlon

Each time I see her, she is wearing a different pair of shoes. Tonight, they are shiny. Patent leather. I'm jealous of her shoes. I've watched her every day for three days out of a week for four months. She's stood in the same place each time and traced a half moon on the station platform with the toe of a flat shoe until the train arrives. She glides up the steps into the carriage – even when the train comes in slightly before or slightly behind what I assume is its designated stopping point. Yet despite me watching her feet, I never see any significant movement either to her left or to her right.

I gradually move closer to her. For two weeks, I've loitered nearby, ready to climb on board alongside her. I have marked the spot like a dog. There's the crumpled flagstone at the edge where the warning line has worn out and the rut collects water. When it's raining hard, I hold back because a puddle will have formed. But I know when to surge forward, split seconds ahead of them calling the arrival, and I always find a seat. Even so, I never see her once I've pulled myself up with the handrail and look around. I never see her, until the same time, the next whenever day it is, because it's not always tomorrow. I wonder what shoes she wears on the other days. I wonder if she takes the same size as me.

CITY TOUR

Stuart Larner

The river slinks through the city, oozing in afternoon heat, feeding monuments with its blood, carrying secrets so old and deep only it has seen. Only it could know.

I take another sip at my riverside table.

A pleasure boat hums into view, large-windowed, labelled 'See the City!' People sit in rows, staring out, as still as flowers in their floating greenhouse where commentary bathes them like the sun.

Smooth white boatskin cleaves the surface, churning the cream of history's milk.

The engine sloshes as they pass. At the stern, a single flag salutes each monument ticked off their list. Memories will lap like lullabies.

The boat turns behind a building.

At its stern some strangers wave to me.

I raise my glass.

They raise an iphone, just as the boat disappears.

I pose long after they have gone, wondering if the picture was taken.

THE CALL OF THE SEA

Aisling Keogh

The city welcomed me in as though I were a long-lost cousin, come in search of his roots.

Street artists played tunes that raised me up to the sun, and the bodhran's beat drummed its music into my bones, while I drank pints of porter and watched hen parties wobble on cobblestone streets.

And then watched, as night fell, a dozen or so men, big and burly, in orange high visibility jackets – padded, waterproof – like vigilantes patrolling I didn't know what. With their benign smiles and idle talk, their presence didn't signal a threat the same way the police force did at home.

'That's because they're not the police,' my dreadlocked drinking companion told me.

'Then what are they?' I asked.

'Water patrol,' he said, matter-of-factly.

'I'm sorry?'

At first, I didn't understand. When you grow up in a country that's landlocked, you can comprehend the call of the mountains, but not the call of the sea.

'There's a couple of bridges this end of town,' he said, as he stood to move towards the bar, again. 'They patrol them.'

I nodded as though I knew what he meant, but really I was thinking back to heated discussions around my grandparents' kitchen table. Frayed tempers and cross words about rod licences and salmon fishing, back when I was young enough to wear cord trousers of my mother's choosing.

After swallowing the dregs from that last one he bought, we stopped into a takeaway and ate vinegar-soaked chips, like the ones Mum used to make, as we strolled to a taxi rank, and I counted them along the way.

Counted four posters, of four young men, all smiling for the camera, now 'missing' since April 4th, May 15th, July 19th, October 27th.

No more than arctic dwellers have hundreds of words for snow, this city has many words to describe rain. It's a *soft day* when the rain-mist blows horizontal in off the sea, instead of falling in globulous drops from the sky. Damp-chilled to the bone, still clinging to the protective warmth of a tray of deep-fried potato, I shuddered as a coolness spread from my neck to behind my ears, and it shook me awake.

Those men in orange jackets were not there to stymie poachers, they were there to fight the tide. To stop it bringing another young man home.

My urge was to run, anywhere but here, at a taxi stand, with rain blowing the hard truth. I could run to a bridge, climb its railings. Test the city's force of orange peacekeepers. But I hadn't air enough in my lungs to act, so I stood. Frozen. Remotely viewing the crowds as they walked on past those posters, as if it was normal. Inevitable. And on the short taxi ride home, I couldn't help but wonder – am I safe?

HOTELS

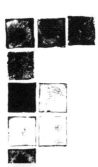

THE RIGHT PLACE

Rosamund Davies

When we return to the hotel, it is no longer here.

The taxi dropped us off here that morning, we think… we're pretty sure, we hope… and there is a hotel here and it looks like our hotel, but it does not have the name of our hotel.

So we look at the dot on our phone and we find that we are almost in the right place, but not quite. We need to move up the street a bit.

So we move up the street until we reach the dot. But the dot is not in the right place. It marks an empty shop that we do not recognise at all.

So we ask a passerby, who tells us that the place we are looking for is not in this street at all.

So we turn right and right again and find another street with another hotel that has the right name.

But this hotel does not look like our hotel. Has our hotel got bored in our absence and swapped names with the hotel in the next street? Has it reproduced or split into two? How can we get our hotel back into the right place? And what tricks will it play on us tomorrow?

LIFTED

Jane Roberts

As you lie in bed in the executive hotel room that was an upgrade because you complained about your original room not overlooking the garden, you are kept awake by the rumblings of the lift – straps and cogs and hydraulics throbbing and graunching. It occurs to you that the hotel must be an exceptionally busy hotel, and, therefore, you have picked a good hotel. The thought is almost enough to send you into a contented sleep. Almost. It does not occur to you that the hotel reception staff are pressing the lift buttons on the ground floor all night long.

YOUR BRAND OF SMOKES

Jesse Sensibar

I'm leaned up against the old cigarette machine that hulks in the shadows to the right of the main door to the bar of the lounge, almost underground in the bottom of the old hotel. I'm up against the big machine because it's about the only place left to stand in the crowded, smoky bar.

The machine and me are the only two things not moving in the place. The music is hard and fast and the crowd moves pogo-style with it.

I've got a lot of love for this cigarette machine. My grandfather was one of the first Marlboro Men.

It's so old it is mechanical instead of being electronic. It jams every once in a while but it mostly works pretty flawlessly. You pick your brand of smoke from the pictures on the face of the machine and put your coins in the slot. Below each picture is a small round chrome knob decorated and edged with tiny scallops. You grab the knob and pull, the knob comes out towards you a full ten or twelve inches on a steel slide with a sound like working a long action on a 12 gauge pump shotgun. It makes the same resounding chunk, when your pack of cigarettes falls out of the machine and into the tray below, as a shotgun does when it chambers another shell.

TWO TILL FOUR

Liam Hogan

She stretched out on the rumpled linen, listening to the shower from the hotel en suite. There was something indolent about sex in the afternoon. The knowledge that everyone else was at their desks, staring at spreadsheets or unravelling corporate memos, minds dulled by a snatched lunch.

She'd be one of them if she hadn't, some four months earlier, invented a weekly therapy session. She'd never specified what the therapy was and her boss had been too nervous to pry. Presumably he thought she was seeing a shrink.

He can't have been disappointed with the results. On Tuesdays, both after and before her appointment, she was relaxed and simultaneously more focused. Whether it was the sex or simply the midday timeout, she often returned with the solution to a tricky problem, or a new direction for her team to take.

Her lover didn't have any difficulty getting away either. One of the perks of being freelance. Or self-unemployed, as he joked when things weren't going so well. She didn't mind paying for the room; a block booking made it indecently affordable.

She'd have offered to pay for his time as well but it was best to keep the arrangement simple.

Light filtered through the net curtain, the sounds of traffic mixing with drowsy birdsong. The pump cut off, restarting a minute later. The time it took him to shampoo. He always seemed slightly too eager to jump into the shower after sex. But he was a considerate lover in all other regards and, after all, they only had an hour together. An hour and a quarter if she was lucky with public transport.

Still, she was thankful for these stolen moments, while the sensations were still fresh, the memory almost overwhelming.

She'd thought, once or twice, about letting herself be impregnated, but he'd make a lousy husband. Insecure about the disparity in their salaries, in their positions. He might, she admitted, make a decent enough father, but shackled together they'd both grow resentful. She could always go it alone. Not yet, though; her career wasn't quite where she wanted it to be.

He wandered back in, sporting a white towel.

'I'll need to rebook,' she commented.

'Don't bother,' he replied, uncharacteristically abrupt.

She propped herself up, feeling the cotton pull at her damp skin. 'Oh?'

'I've got a new job. A full-time one.'

'Some alternative arrangement?' she suggested, as he dried his legs.

He shook his head. 'No. It's been... lovely. But this is just a distraction, isn't it? An interlude.'

'A good distraction, I trust?'

He smiled, shrugged. 'The best.'

At the office she stared at the cluster of emails clamouring for attention. Noise. Just... useless noise. Zoned in on a meeting request, a week in advance, organised by her opposite number. She checked the scheduled time: two-thirty. The bitch.

She could keep the pretence going. Find another partner. It wouldn't be so very difficult.

Angrily she stabbed *Accept*.

STARLIGHT

C.A. Limina

There *is* one. A single one. A lone white dot on a black carpet, the last soldier standing in an old war. It flickers and reflects off the hotel window, and as he blurs the glass with his breath, he wonders if there was any other alternative.

The city flickers and beats like a cosmic being, thrumming with sounds and smells and light – all the light missing from the heavens. The stillness of the hotel room feels like the sterility of a space pod, protecting him from all the light and darkness and void that lies outside the window.

The humming of the air conditioner drives him mad. The unperturbed duvet, the soft yellow glowing from beneath the walls, the bathroom door leading into otherworldly white lights and porcelain surfaces, the fact that nobody but his boss is going to call him and ask how his business trip is going, it's all maddening. It reminds him that he hasn't had a good night of sleep in twenty years. He'd thought that if he got a promotion, or made a name for himself, or slept in a five-star hotel with decent internet reception, it would've got better, but it didn't. He couldn't sleep. Not while the city was awake.

How does that star feel?

How does it feel, watching grassy plains suddenly morph into glass and asphalt? How does it feel to be somewhere other than this hotel, this sterile pod protecting him from the smog and corruption and noise? How does it feel to be a dull dot on a black night, staring down at an ephemeral flash of light and madness?

His hands leave marks on the clear glass, and he knows this is the highest he'll ever be. The closest he'll ever be to a star. The hotel vibrates beneath his feet, and he can feel the hollow in his chest, the ringing in his ears, the cracking of his bones. *Sleep,* he thinks. *Just a little sleep. That's all I need.*

So he does. He pulls the handle of his little space pod, letting the car honks and pollution seep into the vacuum. He dreams of falling into a distant star, watching as the light of the city flickers in the distance. He smiles. And he sleeps.

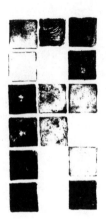

TRANSPORT

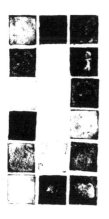

COFFEE

Shamini Sriskandarajah

She sits opposite me, holding her coffee in both hands but not touching her piece of cake that sits on the table, wrapped in paper. The cake I laboured over last night, the cake that was supposed to make this journey smoother for us.

She is not going to give me a break. She will sit there until the train gets to our station, staring out of the window, slowly sipping her coffee. The coffee that a stranger made in a few minutes. But she won't touch the cake that took me two hours.

NOT EVERY TRAIN

Jasmin Kirkbride

The train is mine. It is where I eat breakfast and apply my face, where I sleep off work, so that I can put on 'bright and merry' for my family who don't like seeing dark rings. It is where I dream about my worries and desires. It is where I laugh and cry at dog-eared books and earnest podcasts that I wouldn't otherwise have time for.

The train is my home. *Mine.* Partly because in the anonymous commuter hour, nobody is watching me, not on an inner-city train. The grind of the rails is a static safety-net for the introverted and over-worked. This is where we can be ourselves. Sometimes we just stare vacantly out of the window or into our laps. A communal exercise designed for the individual.

Although the route I take is the same each day, the trains themselves vary. Yet the extruded plastic seats and psychedelic fabric designs are repeated with such uncanny similarity, that it is as if all trains are connected by a thread of time and space, so that when I lean against a glass partition for support, I am leaning against all glass partitions on every train, being held by each of those huge and indestructible machines, their collective consciousness speaking in a Morse code of hurrying railway sleepers, speaking to each other, and to me.

They tell me I am safe, that there will always be a destination for me. That if I board at A, B will soon arrive. For me, the railways are a measure of control, a way to contain the labyrinthine city that swings ever further out of my hands. As long as I belong to the trains, I know where I'm going.

But slowly, I realise the trains operate beyond my knowledge. At night, I hear them – my train, and its siblings – ricocheting from borough to borough, their squeals as drivers brake them too hard, or their galloping laughter as they haul freights and passengers. I sense them other places too: their thunder shaking the ground under my feet in the park, or the tell-tale crack of overhead wires beyond a row of houses. Sometimes just a far-off horn and a whisper of track: *shuck-shuck, shuck-shuck-shuck…*

Obsessively, I try to trace every one of them, catch them and memorise their timetables, so that I can speak their language fluently. But they cannot all be found. I hear trains even when I know there can't be any, unknown ghosts on lines that do not exist. Imagined heartbeats in the cadaver metropolis growing around me.

And I have to relinquish myself to the greater master of us all: the city itself, which we cannot avoid, and which forces us to make the cold and lonely steel of the trains our home.

THE SECOND CAR FROM THE FRONT

Alexandra Penland

They have spent forty-five minutes together every day for five years. It begins as a ritual: each arriving at the platform to catch the 7:15 in a state of slight agitation. Tapped toes on octagonal brick. Checked watches. Picked-at nails. The train arrives like a silver dragon and swallows them alive: a young professional woman, a man in his daily suit, a person of indiscriminate gender who clearly works in the tech industry, an older gentleman in a museum docent's uniform. They take their seats, always in the second car from the front. In five years, it is a routine they know by heart.

They have never spoken to each other.

The techie sports a hoodie and headphones. They started wearing cargo shorts sometime in the 90s and never stopped, and their hair changes colours with the season. The museum docent enjoys colourful bow ties. The man in a suit has been, for the past five years, slightly irritated by the docent's garish taste, but the techie enjoys them immensely, and often comments to their friends at work on what colour or pattern the docent wore that morning. The young, professional woman is serious and works in finance, and she does not have an opinion on the bow ties: for her the commute is meditative, spent half-asleep to the classical music that plays through white earbuds.

The man stands near the door. The techie is rude and steals two seats, one for themselves and one for their backpack. The woman likes to sit on the right side, staring out the window that does not look at walls. The docent refuses to use the accessible seating, choosing instead to sit near the back of the car. When possible, he always chooses the same spot.

Each day they are surrounded by others, by tourists and transients and school trips. Occasionally someone joins them for a time, but new riders never seem to last. Their commute changes, or they start sitting in a different car. Some days a preacher or performer will intrude, calling for the residents to seek forgiveness from sin, or pay with small change for drums that no one asked to hear. On such occasions the riders exchange frustrated glances.

Sometimes the train is delayed, and they are forced to wait in the tunnels. Once the train was delayed for two and a half hours. The man nearly broke a window trying to call his job. They had no cell service in the car.

The techie was the first to notice when the docent stopped riding. The woman noticed next, then the young man. There was no way to learn *why* things had changed. They did not know each other. Perhaps he had moved. Retired for good. Died.

When a tourist tried to take the docent's seat, it was the woman who intervened. Then the techie, two stops later. Then the man. They said the same thing, instinctively.

'Sorry. We're saving it for someone.'

SLIM ODDS

Laura Besley

Eight point seven million people in this city and I realise
I'm sitting opposite my sister. I'm travelling north on one
of the older underground trains. What are the odds? She's
reading (some things never change) a paperback with a
colourful cover of abstract shapes. She turns the page,
slowly, letting the words soak into her. Not like me; I read
quickly, greedily, eager to find out what happens next. We
were always different in that way.

I study her shorter hair, now showing a few strands
of grey; her thicker frame clad in an oversized woollen
turtleneck and sensible black trousers; and her face which
is essentially the same, but with a few more lines around
her eyes. *Don't look up,* I think.

We haven't spoken in years. Most of the time I manage to
lock the feelings of hurt and hatred in a box and bury it deep
inside, but every now and then the lid creaks open and I
am overwhelmed by a sadness that leaves me feeling bereft
for days. Money was the cause of it all. When I look back
I can't believe I was stupid enough to fall out over money.

The train rattles on, clacking along the tracks, alternating
between darkness and light as we move in and out of
stations and I try to decide whether to talk to her or not. I
keep thinking I should, but then remember that I haven't
moved in five years and not once has she contacted me;
no birthday card or Christmas card or phone call. Is she
still not ready to talk? Last year I walked by her house

to find a different family eating dinner behind the sash windows and was stabbed by the realisation that she had moved without letting me know.

Bland tiles and the familiar station logo come into view and the train slows. I take a breath and tell myself that when we pull out of this station, I will reach out to her. Suddenly she jumps out of her seat and rushes out of the train, clutching her book in one hand and her bag in the other. As she does, her gaze runs over my face, but I can't be certain she has registered my familiar features.

The doors close and I stand up, better to see her walk down the platform. She turns her head and looks back into the train. Now she sees me. Is that a smile I see as the train pulls away? Maybe I'll never know.

OTHER SIGNALS

Annabel Banks

Four stops left and I'd limp home faster than this elephantine, nose-to-tail traffic. But I've paid my fare, already hit my ten thousand steps, so what the hell. Bottom on seat, skirt tucked under, shoulder to metal, to purring glass. I breathe lightly, scroll my phone: *leave me alone.*

The man next to me is fastidious in his untouching; I sense the tension in his pressed-together thighs, blue trousers so tight they could be body paint.

He scrolls his phone, too. *I leave you alone lady don't care about you.*

I love him.

Three stops. The sense of others presses in. Passengers droop over bars, tightly bound or unapologetically spread, depending on their mass and temperament. The city is refusing to release the day's heat, prickling top lips, staining backs and sticking flopped hair to foreheads. A woman talks, all liquid language and spasming hands that graze the collar of the man in front. She seems angry, but I've big-citied for long enough now to know that's her-as-me, not her-as-her.

Seven on, five off. The man next to me leaves.

Four off, six on, to settle like sieved flour. My seat is towards the rear.

I am alone. Scroll, scroll. Breathe lightly. Love.

Three off. One on: an old lady with a kerfuffle of bags. Bright red hat, woollen skirt, wet-faced and gasping. She approaches my kingdom of one-on-a-seat and makes the signals of intent, the uncaught eye-flick and half-turn to reverse into position. I shuffle my legs, move my shoulders a little, bumping against the trembling wall. There is no more room, but this is a gesture of invitation, a promise to share properly. *Love me. I am safe.*

The woman bumps down heavily, exhales, then bends to scoop the tattered plastic bags onto her lap. Inside, the contents shift and rattle. In a few moments, I will use my side-eye to examine them, curious to see what she's carrying.

She scrunches the necks of the bags, fists tight as a promise. *You may not see.*

Scroll, scroll, turn away. Streets vibrate with the engine, pedestrians blurred into impressions.

One stop to go.

The woman turns her head, all *I see you,* and – oh god – I feel the words gathering. She will ask *What are you reading? Which stop should I get off? Tell me, have you found Jesus?* Or she'll ask me *What's the time?* She might demand some cash. Tell me of her miseries. Of her children and their plans. She'll exclaim *Oh you're so pretty!* She is going to call me damned. She'll ask me *Where's your skirt from?* She will bring a knife from the bag. She will cut me a piece of pineapple. She will stab me in the throat. She will ask if I have daughters. Begin

to chant her day. Produce an unscratched scratchcard:
hey, you got a coin?

Half-stand, hand out. Bing the bell: *I hate I fear I go.*

SCHOOL BUS

Evleen Towey

From the small village, in the black and yellow bus filled with cigarette smoke, they travelled daily to the secondary school in the city. It took over an hour each way. They often had to stand, squashed between the sweaty working men and women. If they had a seat, they read a book, or did their homework. The insides of their shirt collars were dark with grime each night.

But they noticed a wider world through the windows of the bus. City people walking purposefully to their offices; hairstyles like on the telly; wearing fashionable clothes like in the magazines. Occasionally, expensive cars like a Rolls Royce with a personalised number plate swept by. There was money in the city.

Eventually making new friends, they used their bus passes on a Saturday: swimming in the Olympic-sized pool, fearlessly jumping off the twenty five metre board; going 'round the shops', dreaming of buying a knickerbocker glory in the café where the rich kids went after school. Some parents even held accounts for their children in the department stores, so they could buy whatever clothes they liked. Jealousy and camaraderie walked hand in hand.

After they outgrew window shopping, they took the bus to the theatre: ten of them turning up for an evening performance – still in their school uniforms – then queueing at the stage door for the actors' autographs. The city cinema showed foreign films and once or twice, they were allowed to go to a pop concert.

Next they were special bussed to the nearby boys' school: a weekly debating club (for grand ideas); a termly disco (for snogging). One early morning in a cream and red single-decker, the hiking club took them out of the city to the hills. They could look back at the smog and the factories, see the spires of churches and cathedrals, wonder and worry about the smoke from the hospital incinerator.

A special bus took them to Prize Night at City Hall, with the mayor handing out book tokens and sound advice. They sang their hearts out on the school song. They will never forget those words.

Then they were gone, as far away as possible, to other university cities.

They've been back, of course, for their reunions: by train, by car and by taxi to the wine bars and restaurants. But there's rubble where the chapel was, and a prefab on the playing field. City Hall looks naked, cleaned of its sooty cloak. The skyscrapers have copulated and brought forth. The hills have receded, like their hair.

One day a smartly dressed Professor looked up and saw, sitting on a bus, the ghost of the girl she used to be. They smiled at each other, understanding that the bus had lifted them up out of the village and set them on their feet. They'd been planted like seeds in the city, where they were fed and where they flowered, casting their pollen to the wind and grey skies.

CAFÉS

COFFEE MEETING

Stuart Larner

Sitting at a table in the café under the escalator, he thumbs through the morning paper. Behind him, in the main body of the café, he hears the hiss and roar of the coffee machine.

The coffee smell permeates the entire small shopping centre, connecting all who will meet this morning through this perfumed medium. Hardly perfume. It is a strong, leaning-forward of the air against his mind, coaxing an expectation.

There is a distant clink of cups and clatter of spoons from the counter as another tray is laid out. He turns to see who the customer is, but it is not her.

He looks at his watch. He has read somewhere that those who come early to a meeting are generally those that have something important to say, and that those who come late generally do not want to hear it.

He checks himself from being unduly paranoid about her absence. There is no guarantee that his apology the other night would have got through.

He takes a long time drinking the coffee, but at last his cup is empty. With a sigh of resignation, he picks up his heavy bag from the chair opposite him, the place that he had been saving. He walks over to the escalator. As he ascends, he surveys the whole centre. There is some quick movement in the crowd down the entrance slope below. A woman is rushing towards the coffee bar. It is her.

He wants to run down the escalator to her, but it has carried him too far up. By the time he reaches the top, he can no longer see her. He rushes through the crowds along the upper mall, dodging the pushchairs, and takes the escalator back down. He is stuck behind a couple standing side by side blocking a step, but he leaps past them at the bottom to hurry across to the café. He catches up with her breathlessly as she reaches the counter.

'You're late – as usual,' she says.

EAVESDROPPING

Rosamund Davies

Hello.   *Coffee.*   Yes.   NICE TO SEE YOU.
I'm giving up next week.   *Yes please.*   Two.
SAME AGAIN?   Next Monday.   *How much?*
Why, what did he say to you?   *I don't think I can.*
I WISH I'D DONE SOMETHING TO HELP.
Did you?   And what's your favourite colour?
BUT WHAT COULD YOU HAVE DONE?
I can't, I absolutely can't.   *I can't stand her.*
Oh well, colours aren't that important.
WHAT ELSE DO YOU LIKE?   I don't know what to do.
I can't do you much of a deal if that's all you want.
Have you been on a lot of dates?   STRONG.   No sugar.
How are things?   I SHOULD HAVE DONE SOMETHING.
I'll take an ounce.
I like to get to know somebody, it's not all about looks.
With cream.   Maybe.   *Let's keep in touch.*
I KEEP TELLING YOU, IT'S NOT YOUR FAULT.
Nobody told me.   Taste this.   *Drink up.*
What's done is done and maybe it's for the best.   TEA.
I'll always blame myself, I can't help it.   *With lemon.*
I hope you find what you're looking for.
Have you been here before?
See you soon.   GOODBYE.
Shall we go?

A QUARTER GLASS OF WINE

Jayne Buxton

Normally I'd have preferred to sit outside where you can watch the people go by and try to feel a part of the city. But it was so stinking hot that I was glad to be inside. (You'll never feel a part of that city, my father had said when I'd told him I was moving. It's a filthy, noisy madhouse, he said, full of ill-mannered people.)

The place was empty except for the barman and a waitress. I ordered a glass of wine. A woman shuffled in, skinny and frail. She had to be ninety years old.

'Hey!' said the waitress.

'Hey there,' said the barman. 'I got your table waiting.'

'Is it hot enough for you?' the woman asked, as she made her way to the table next to mine.

'So what'll it be today?' the waitress asked her.

'That chicken dish, is it made with cream?'

'A little cream, I believe.'

'I thought so. I can't have cream because I need to lose a couple of pounds.'

'You trying to disappear?' the barman called out.

'I put on two pounds.'

'That's good,' the waitress said.

'No, it's not good. I need to lose them. What do you eat?'

'This one, she eats sweets all day,' said the barman, gesturing to the waitress.

'It's true, I eat sweets all day.'

'Well if I moved around like you, I'd eat sweets all day too. But I don't move. I sit in my apartment. They say don't go out in this heat, so I don't. And I gained two pounds.'

'You look great though,' said the barman.

'No, I have to lose them. What else have you got besides the chicken?'

'The lentil salad is nice. It's new,' the waitress said.

'Lentils?'

'It's nice,' said the barman.

'Okay, bring me the lentil salad.'

'You want a glass of wine with that?'

'Just a quarter glass. If you give me a whole one, I'll drink it.'

'Oh, I know you will.'

The waitress brought the quarter glass of wine.

'Another one?' she said to me.

'I'm not sure I have time. I'm waiting for a call about an appointment.'

'Good excuse for another glass of wine,' she said.

'Okay then. One more.'

She brought me another glass. Minutes later, my phone beeped.

'I have to go,' I said.

'Oh no, you can't finish your wine?' the waitress said, making a sad face.

She brought me the bill and I paid with cash.

'Come back and see us,' the barman called out as I stood to leave.

Out on the street the heat hit me with the force of a freight train. I walked towards my appointment, wondering if the woman at the table next to mine would be persuaded to have another quarter glass of wine. Then I thought about my father, drinking his wine alone in that chair of his, no one trying to persuade him of anything.

THE PROMISE

Reshma Ruia

'The cappuccino is piping hot, just the way I like it.'

'Yes, and my orange juice tastes of sunshine,' my wife agrees, as we compliment the waiter who stands by our table, holding a silver tray. He is a young boy, barely out of his teens, slim of build, with fingers long and lean.

We resume our conversation, switching from English to our own language, but the waiter is lingering. He is fiddling with the bill, unsure whether to place it on our table or wait for us to finish our drinks. I glance at him again. It is obvious that looking at us, he feels a kinship of colour and language.

'He must be homesick,' I whisper to my wife. She nods and turns to him.

'Have you been here long?' She speaks to him in our language, her voice gentle and enquiring.

His shoulders relax and his mouth creases into a u-shaped smile.

'I came here six months back and found this job. This is peak season and they needed an extra pair of hands.' He glances around to check whether the manager has spotted him chatting with us, but he is busy at another table, fawning over a group who have ordered bottles of champagne.

'Are you from…?' I mention the name of our city. He shakes his head and says he is from another small city close to the border.

I remember his city. I used to go there as a child. It was by the sea and in the summer was crowded with people strolling under the palm trees, sipping coconut water or eating watermelon slices, the juice painting their lips red. This was before the war. Now most of it lies shrouded under gunfire mist with houses half-fallen, their roofs ripped apart, open to the sky.

'You were lucky to escape,' I lower my voice. Most young men in that city have disappeared, buried in nameless graveyards.

'My mother told me I had to get out. She didn't want me to join the army.' He grins, but his eyes cloud over as he says this.

My wife leans over and pats his arm. I know she is remembering our own kids, busy pursuing their university degrees and dreams. This boy, standing here in his shiny black trousers with frayed hems, and polished but worn out black shoes, could be them.

'Well you've chosen a beautiful city to start afresh,' I say.

The café is on the main square. Immediately on our right stands the cathedral, proudly majestic and the fountain nearby is gurgling happily. Tired and hot tourists perch on its ledge, dipping their bare toes into the cool water.

'Good luck,' I say and pay the bill, slipping in a more than generous tip.

He presses his right hand to his heart and thanks us.

'Don't do this forever,' my wife says as we leave. 'Become a doctor or an engineer and rebuild your city.'

'I promise,' he says.

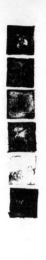

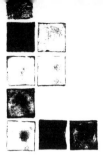

MAIN STREETS

SWITCHING ON
Kam Rehal

THIS   PLACE   IS   OPEN   COME   ON   IN

THIS   SPACE   IS   OPEN   COME   ON   IN

THIS   PLACE   IS   OPEN   COME   ON   IN

THIS   PLACE   IS   OPEN   COME   ON   IN

THIS   PLACE   IS   OPEN   COME   ON   IN

THIS   SPACE   IS   OPEN   COME   ON   IN

THIS   PLACE   IS   OPEN   COME   ON   IN

THIS   PLACE   IS   OPEN   COME   ON   IN

THIS   PLACE   IS   OPEN   COME   ON   IN

WALKING BACK TO THE FUTURE

Máire Malone

The photographer clicks a snapshot of a daughter linking arms with her father, as they cross the three-arch bridge with its sandstone balustrades and ornate lampstands. Their cheeks bulge with barley sugar sweets as they make their way to catch a train to the sea, north of the city.

They pass memorials to politicians and martyrs and a building pock-marked with bullets. They hear echoes of a poet reading a proclamation of independence. The smell of gunfire lingers. The legacy of dead men was freedom.

They crane their necks to see the famous clock and the column where a statue stands: a navy officer who was wounded in combat.

In the same year the statue is blown up, a garden in the shape of a sunken cruciform water-feature is created to remember the Vision.

The father will not see the high, stainless-steel, pin-like monument of light – but the daughter will.

FLOTSAM AND JETSAM

Cathy Lennon

'Wherever there is people there is dirt. Wherever there is dirt there is money. Wherever there is money there is people.'

The street sweeper likes to repeat the mantra to himself. It keeps him in a Zen state of mind, even as the crowds start to build. In the morning, early, the streets belong to him and he sometimes hums.

He ignores the bodies lying in the doorways and they ignore him. He does not touch their paper cups, their plastic bags. There are plenty more.

Food cartons waft in the gutters, cigarette butts eddy beneath the exhaust fumes. It's like an ocean, he thinks. A tide that shifts and swells and washes something up each day.

Sometimes he breaks into a song. Just a few notes, a few words from back home. He hoists his cart and broom and trundles on, cresting the waves.

YOU STAND IN THE SECRET PLACE

Steven Wingate

Every city has its secret places and you are standing in one and all you have to do is believe this and stay completely still and feel the rush of passers-by likё the wind or take pictures of things that are incomprehensible to you or of mundane things your eye makes miraculous or walk at exactly the right speed to make the secret place open up and swallow you.

None of these secret places will reveal themselves if you are looking for them and yes this is the most unbearable thing in life and yes the secret places know this and they do not care if you are frustrated and yes your frustration can transport you into a rapture that sufficiently appeases the secret places and coaxes them into opening themselves to you on a whim and yes this is what people fail to understand when they claim that cities are temples of utilitarianism without magic.

When you are swallowed up by a city's secret place you will know exactly what to do because you have earned the right to be subsumed by it and be made one with it and you know that each secret place has its own unique appropriate supplicating action and you will perform it perfectly whether that action is to whirl in a circle with your arms at your sides or to open your mouth and receive the hidden word or to fall ever backwards with no need to be caught.

And then the city will be yours, and you will be the city's.

HOW TO GO WITH THE FLOW:
A SURVIVAL GUIDE

Arna Radovich

The key to survival is walking fast. Has anyone ever told you that, specifically, explicitly? Since its humble beginnings, I've seen my city grow into what you see before you, in all its glittery glory. I see people circulating through the arteries, veins and capillaries of my streets and roads, my boulevards and twisting lanes of tar and concrete, cobblestone and granite. I see them neatly side-step those who huddle on footpaths, avoiding the disturbed drifters, the backpacker charity-collectors and the trouble-makers who try to stop them in their tracks with alternative narratives that do not fit with how this great city of mine likes to see itself. Fencing and feinting my people parry, in constant motion, for they have learnt the lesson that it can be dangerous to stop – the current can pull you under and, more likely than not, there will be *no* handsome bronzed life-saver to charge into the surf and administer the kiss of life. The city is no place for immobility. No pausing to chat about the weather, or offer a few moments of warm communication to one of the isolated souls who squat, backs against the wall. Not on my streets, no siree! Go back to your village if you want that, your small parochial town, your dying rural backwater where there is plenty of time but not much else. I know I'm biased, but still, you came here for excitement, remember? For the intoxication of speed and collective energy, the high-tension buzz of too many people in one place at one time, scurrying, dare I say, a bit like rats.

A certain behaviour develops, whether you like it or not, I see it all the time – it's a kind of survivor syndrome – a pulling up of the drawbridge, a hardening of the outer shell of self. If every sad story, every person curled in a ragged sleeping bag on a freezing street pierces your heart, you'll never make it. Take your life in your hands along with your double strength almond latte and move along now, fast as you can. It's best not to divert your attention to those at the edges, washed up by the tide. If you pause and ponder for too long, your brain could explode, because, if it's true what evolutionary psychologist Robin Dunbar says, humans can only maintain relationships with a limited amount of people – five in the innermost circle, a hundred and fifty at the outer limit – and therefore, it is pure folly to gift your time or care to the multitude of random people you pass each day, because there is no way they can be realistically accommodated within your circle. You must know this – it's city living 101. So, post an inspirational Instagram or, better still, a quick tweet to remind yourself to keep your thinking within the lines, look straight ahead, go with the flow and don't stop, whatever you do – that's how you navigate to survive in my city. Don't say you weren't warned.

BETWEEN SKYSCRAPERS

Wes Lee

The vortex around you dissolving
   like the last drops of something.
When rain is easing.
When snow is stopping.
When all the icicles have fallen.
When all the fish have slapped from the
   clouds onto the roofs of station wagons.

DAWN OF THE CITY

Nicholas McGaughey

The sun is out with the sweepers,
there's been no frost.
8am on a November Sunday,
with the seagulls strutting on the bridge
and nobody much about,
bar a smudged zombie and a werewolf quaking
in a doorway.

By the brown tiled tap-room
there are no buses,
the pavement greased
with slid kebabs
and a flower of sick
by the all-night caff
where breakfast is served.

The ticket dispensers… don't,
as last night's stragglers,
with eyes like currants,
exaggerate their evenings,
and wend their way back
to whatever welcomes await them,
where fried eggs are stared at behind broadsheets,
before stairs, and the flimsy parapet of a glaring bed.

SEEING IN THE DARK

Roland Denning

There is nowhere to hide down these streets, no back alleys, no shadowy corners, now the cameras can see in the dark. There are cameras in my living room. I know they're in yours too.

A reasonable man would accept we need them gazing down on us, keeping our streets safe. But you know I'm not a reasonable man.

'There's nothing to fear if you do nothing wrong,' they used to say.

'But if I'm doing nothing wrong, why are you watching me all the time?' I'd shout back.

And shouting back at machines never improves your public standing. Particularly now the machines can hear.

You must have noticed how the rise in 'reality' TV accompanied the spread of security cameras. Every place of work is a studio, every home a set. Everyone can be a TV star. Funny we never get to meet the director, or have a say in the cut.

You must agree the judge's summing up recognised my low-tech ingenuity; the myriad ways I found to blind the cameras, from wire snips and air rifles to spray guns on poles and clusters of floating, glue-soaked balloons (the hydrogen ones were the best – they exploded so sweetly). Her revenge was to allow me to be confined at home, monitored and surveilled by the latest technology. The state is acquiring a taste for irony.

I remember when people were glad when the cameras went up; they were afraid of the belligerent youths hanging around on street corners. Then as time went on it became clear that they weren't all youths, and as jobs got scarcer, the 'them' became 'us'. The strange thing is, I've always been a loner but, lately, I've found myself on the side of the mob.

Unreasonable, ingenious and quaintly old-style, that's me. The way I see it, planting a small amount of explosive in the right place is healthier than sitting at home writing viruses. Gets you out and about. The technocrats would like you to believe that everything that matters now takes place in the virtual world, but really it all begins with a box of tangled wires and a camera waiting to be smashed. Good old-fashioned violence gets the job done.

At night I have this dream. Down the street the blank walls give nothing away, but I look up to the roofs and chimneys, jet black against a dark mauve sky, and, higher still, the posts on which the cameras peer and listen. Now I see them burning as orange flames lick their lenses. The cameras crackle and spit, then break apart; from their guts a thick, dark residue oozes to the ground. I cannot see into the other houses, but I know you are there, waiting.

Soon we will break through the walls, you and I, we will drive beyond these dim streets, across hills and rivers, never to be seen again.

I LEFT THE CITY THAT NIGHT

Pedro Basso Neves

I left home that night
thinking that I was going to die.
My heart was pounding.

(I've got a weak heart)

I've got a weak heart
like my grandfather who died young.
My oldest memory is of the day he died.
I remember my mother crying
and my father taking me outside.

(I'm outside)

I walked the main street with my eyes fixed
before my feet,
bowed under the weight of my thoughts.
My heart was pounding.
Restlessly. Out of control.

(Am I going to die?)

I felt that death was close by. Waiting...

Tiptap – Tiptap – Tiptap

And then suddenly,
amidst the murmur of thoughts,
I heard the regular cadence of my own footsteps.

Tiptap – Tiptap – Tiptap

And slowly,
with each step,
Tiptap
my unsteady heart
Tiptap
found its pace.

(I have to keep walking)

And so I left the city that night.

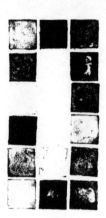
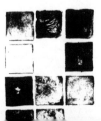

MARKET

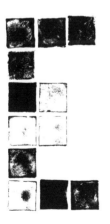

THE CITY'S HEARTBEAT

Emma Lee

The market is a measure of a city's heartbeat. Usually smell hits you first. Hopefully fresh produce: earthy vegetables, a sweet note of fruit, a tang of leather and maybe a whiff of freshly-brewed coffee, a sizzle of fried onions, a smear of strawberries tantalise taste buds. Sounds are a second clue. Do stall-holders chatter and joke? Do they call out to attract passers-by? Do shoppers slow their pace to browse? Textures invite touch: a stiff net, a soft fake fur, the shine on a waxed apple, the silk on a satin orchid or the smoothness of painted wood. Sight reveals a whirl of colour, smiles, space for a breather from a nagging list of errands, a toddler jumping in puddles, laughter from gossips.

In some, the smells are marred by a sour note of decay under disinfectant, the freshly-brewed coffee can't compete with a stench of rot. Stall-holders are silent and hunched with hands in pockets or cupped around a brew. Passers-by speed up: nothing to see here. Children whine and pester, reluctant to stop. Colours fade to neutrals: greys and beiges of institutions. Glares deter touching. Products are displayed under covers or still inside boxes. Pedestrians look at their feet to avoid catching another's eye and notice the rubbish piling under stalls, the boxes of produce not unpacked and the unswept dirt. Unwelcomed, they turn away.

Today she feels upbeat, her stride confident, heels tapping to a heartbeat. She has a red jacket and ready smile. She buys fresh to cook a healthy dinner, stops to taste a cool smoothie, lingers over hand-crafted souvenirs. She pauses for a bouquet of silk carnations: nothing showy, but a splash of colour for her table, planned to inspire a sensual evening. She frequently stops to chat, share a joke and leaves on a whirl of inspiration.

Tomorrow she might be back. The red jacket swapped for a beige trench coat. Her steps ponderous. Her eyes darting so they never settle on one thing. She looks, but her purse stays in her bag. The hand-crafted goods have become cheap bric-a-brac. Her perfume is overwhelmed by the stink from uncleared refuse. She has forgotten her smile. Her shoulders sag. When she stops, both hands clasp a cooling coffee, a jumper sleeve is hooked over a thumb but doesn't quite cover a damson-coloured bruise. Her heart is sluggish.

Tomorrow she might be back. Note whether you can smell perfume, whether she smiles and if it meets her eyes, if her walk skips. Is the city as healthy as it thinks?

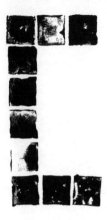

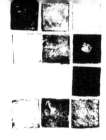

CROSSROADS

FOUNDATION MYTH

Cherry Potts

You stand at the crossroads, or what was once a crossroads, before roads got too dangerous and complicated to cross, requiring roundabouts and underpasses, and you step aside, overwhelmed by the lights and the arrows and the sheer number of speeding metal death machines and retreat to the wall that overlooks the river. You stare at the grey metallic water, splashing gently in the wake of some boat that is already out of sight, beyond the bridge that you could walk across if you wanted to cross the river, but you don't want to cross, you want to get across the mouth of the bridge and continue beside the water. There is an underpass somewhere, but you have yet to find it.

Somewhere, in the silt and debris at the edge of this river there is the print of the foot of the first woman who stepped into the waters and judged it shallow enough to ford, long before the river was squashed into this narrow, deep, rapid course. And somewhere, in crossing the broad shallows, she looked up and caught the glimmer of the tributary stream, and the sweet fold of the hill, the shaded slope and the open beach ahead, and thought – *this is my place.*

If you stand on this bridge at dawn on the longest day of the year when sun up and morning chorus and a soft breeze can still filter through the smog and noise, when the passing cars are rare and the hum of air-conditioning is momentarily unnecessary, you can catch what she saw.

You can imagine her putting down her walking staff and gathering her family, her clan, her tribe, and saying *here is our place*. No need to wander further, here is beauty, here is everything we need, here is defensible.

And because they stopped, and put up fences and then buildings, others, passing, also stopped. A pause to talk became a stop to trade, became a plan to stay with friends, became never leaving, building – and sometimes that *defensible* was put to the test as others came to steal and rape and destroy. Through those meetings and destructions and rebuildings their place grew, and over millennia it grew to this, the crossroads where *you* paused a year ago, a decade ago, longer, and thought, *my place*, and put down your walking staff and stopped to talk, to trade, gradually gathering a family, a clan, a tribe, saying *our place*, and building, and welcoming strangers like me, willing to share.

And that *defensible* sticks in our craw, and we regret that we still think it, all these millennia later. Sometimes you forget that you have not always lived here. Sometimes you need to step into the footprint of the first woman, and see this place, *our* place, anew, and put aside defence for the openness she saw on that opposite shore.

GO DIRECTLY TO GO

Rob Walton

'No, listen. I saw this with my own eyes.'

'Your very own eyes?'

'My very own eyes.'

'Shoot.'

'This plane comes down at the crossroads when people are arriving for work. It's eight, eight-thirty in the morning. The pilot wants to know which way to go.'

'So he asks the people who are arriving for work?'

'Whoah! What's this 'he' asks? The pilot asks. Only the people arriving for work are mixed up with tourists and people who have been partying all night, and the pilot is getting contradictory suggestions. Being told to go north to the park, and 'No, no, you want to go downtown'. Someone else says the river and another person talks about the boho area and the hills. One person recommends staying there and they will fix the pilot a coffee and some bagels.'

'And none of these people ask what the pilot and the plane are doing there?'

'Why should they? This is the city. Things happen.'

'Did anyone see the plane land? Was it somehow just there? I don't know. There are so many gaps.'

'Sure there are. This is the city. There are gaps.'

'And where are the plane and the pilot now?'

'I don't know. Some other crossroads? Some other city?'

AT THE CROSSROADS

Matthew Pountney

At the crossroads, an ancient roadway is caressed by apple-scented shisha and exhaust fumes as it mixes its traffic with the city churn.

An arch, not as majestic as its creators had hoped, hails the car-triumph of consumers. Shunted up here, forgotten on an island, and holding court with ping-pong tables and tourists as they bustle, their bags dangling.

The sun shines through the glass of the jelly statue mob, who recall all the fun of execution and entrails. Nuns watch on, hidden away, remembering the martyrs of that place.

Green summer parks draw us from the frozen relics, through avenues of plane trees and the glittering patience of hotels, while Sunday's corner hecklers decry every prejudice but their own.

Old choices led here and new choices lead away.

CHANCE MEETINGS

Maja Bodenstein

I see her for the first time while I'm still a student, adrift in the haze of youth.

I'm on the subway. The carriage is half-empty, holding only tourists, nannies and me, all caught in the grip of stale air and mid-afternoon lethargy. The noise is deafening; I can only just hear the baby's cry over the screeching metal of wheels on track.

Suddenly the dark windows light up: another train, on one of those rare sections where two tracks run parallel. They are so matched in speed that neither train seems to be moving at all; our trajectories are given away only by the tightness of travellers' grips on the handrails, the shaking, and the noise.

Then I see her. We've never met, and yet I know her intimately – because she is me. She's older, a little paler and a little more worn, but she knows me, too; her eyes say so.

She is dressed to go somewhere, either to a function or perhaps an interview. I wonder if there is someone in her life, to iron out her creases and to lead her to sunlight when she needs it. I realize I pity her. She opens her mouth, perhaps to tell me something – does she think she can bridge the airless void between us? I avert my eyes. I don't want to know.

Then the tracks split, she's swallowed by darkness, and I am left with only my reflection in the window.

★

A few years later, I see me again.

I'm on my way back to work after lunch. My office is near the famous scramble crossing, with its complex systems of lights and sounds. She's on the other side, fidgeting, eager for the lights to change. My heart somersaults.

We pass each other at the very centre of the crossing. I smile, a little frightened she might not recognise me. But after all it's another me; an earlier one. She is fresh, vibrant, burning with an elemental power that I don't recall ever possessing. She is almost past, she still hasn't seen me; I panic and reach out. My hand is inches from her electric yellow sweater when her eyes finally flick up to mine.

They bear a hostile warning. She refuses to know me, to know what she has become. Perhaps it's a general resistance to a society that seeks to consume and shackle her; or perhaps she is repulsed by how I have faded, how my own resistance has eroded, and I have been absorbed. I am ashamed. My hand shrinks back.

The lights change again. Somehow, I arrive at the other side. I have already lost sight of her amongst the flow of the city.

I never saw me again; with each passing year, it becomes less likely that I will. I can't help but wonder: What have I missed out on? What life could I have led if I had had the courage, the willingness to listen?

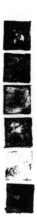

SIDE STREETS

THE ALLEYWAY I

Miriam Sorrentino

My shoes make no
sound on the man–
hole cover under
which water races.
Three bright yellow
dandelions stand to attention along the wall. A mother
in jogging bottoms followed by two little girls with hair
in bunches rounds the corner. The youngest stops and
points to a single abandoned trainer lying on gravel
behind a fence. 'Why is that there?' she asks. Her mother
ignores her and carries on
walking with the eldest.
'It has a name written
inside it, I can see it.'
A man with a dog passes
me, the lead held tight
towards his body. Getting no response the
child runs after her mum. Directly ahead
a procession of ants carries the corpse of a
long dead fly. 'But why was it there?' I walk
on into the dip in
the tarmac that on
rainy days makes the
perfect puddle.

THE ALLEYWAY II

Miriam Sorrentino

A man, hood up, enters the alleyway behind me. My office heels click, click on the tarmac, echoing along the walls. His trainers are almost silent. He picks up his pace. Alone, except for the man, there is no choice but to speed up, click, click, click. He picks up his pace again. I pick up my pace. I reach the lampost at the dead centre of the alleyway. I look up. A spider hangs on a single thread under the bright light. I shake an imaginary stone from my shoe. Looking down I see his old Pumas as he passes. I start to walk – click, click, click – I increase my pace. He picks up his pace slightly. So do I. We can both hear the click of my heels. He picks up his pace. Now I am only two feet behind him. He steps out onto the dark road and looks back startled. Under my hair I smile.

BACKWATER

David Mathews

'Do people fall in?' The young woman called to him over her shoulder.

He had watched her, about his daughter's age, peer in the windows of the houses opposite, all seven, as she walked down the street. She had stopped at the disused granary at the canal's edge. The towpath was on the far side of the water, leaving her no way through.

'Do they?' She walked across to him where he stood outside his door with a coffee pot.

He shook his head. 'Only once, years ago,' he said. 'But the new couple with two kids in number 11 want railings. At Number 7 they'd prefer a wall, but I reckon that could be worse than nothing, because people would walk along it and fall off. Every Friday we argue about it, and then have a drink.'

'They have a playpen in number 11. I think I saw a rat, in the water, not number 11.'

'We don't get many. It's not like a river that brings stuff with the current. With a canal you have to make your own way, and there's no restaurant to attract rats. We had nine ducklings last week, with their mum, but they didn't stop long. We could have a boat, but you can't go far.'

Would she like a coffee?

They sat in the autumn sun on his two kitchen chairs by a square table.

She took off her straw hat, and looked at the sky. 'This is like on holiday somewhere,' she said.

'Last week two tourists ordered espressos.'

'What did you do?'

He had brewed them as ordered, good and strong, and given them cake. 'Thank you waiter,' they had said. When he let on that Number 12 was his home and studio, they insisted on paying him.

She talked to him as a child talks to an adult who shows interest. He asked few questions – his daughter had taught him not to badger people – but he learned that she liked busy places; 'the buzz', she said. She appeared to live out of town, but was vague about where, and did not mention a job or parents or friends, just the countless things she had seen that morning.

'I could stay here,' she said. 'Quiet, but near all that's going on.'

They did not exchange names, but were easy with each other, and she lingered until the sun went behind the houses opposite. He noticed her clothes were shabby.

Next morning he found sandwich crusts in the doorway of the old warehouse; other mornings a paper cup, an empty tobacco pouch, a sock with a hole in the heel.

One night he left a thermos and a cup on his table outside. The following morning, he came out early, hoping. The cup was still warm; beside it lay a coin. His window was smudged, just where she could have pressed her nose against it.

How would she be when the weather grew cold?

ALLEYS AND DUMPSTERS, IN BETWEEN, SUNNY DAY

Patty Tomsky

We walk in full sunlight but people can only see us if they're sad. I don't know why some of us stay. Have you ever heard a voice come up right next to your ear? And no one is there? That's one of us.

If you want to, say a quick prayer that it never happens to you. Counting bricks for centuries, some of us, and moving with anger past babies and people and stores and under a sky from which we never feel the breeze.

I reached a girl the other day, she turned around, she'd been on a shortcut between the giant dustbins behind the pub where she works every weekend. I watched her for a while before I screamed at her back. She felt it. I saw her put her hand up behind her neck like people do when they feel us. Or feel me, at least. I don't talk to the others. I'm afraid.

So, when the sun is bright if it's cold or warm out and you've stepped off this busy sidewalk because you know a back way and then the next thing you know you want to die or begin to remember the dead you've lost or pass through a pocket of ice in the air, don't run. You can't get away.

Seeing us is not like seeing a person, but a cut-out from the sky or a black shadow moving across glass or metal in a back corner of the city where hardly anyone goes but strays or rats or homeless people searching for a place to sleep. Some of them talk to us but we don't talk back. We can't.

If I knew a way for you to avoid becoming like me, I

would tell you. If I knew a way to stop being someone like me, I would do it. I have forgotten my name and the shape of my face but every once in a while, I see a pair of arms I half-remember or, like coming up from deep water, a face from before. I cry but we don't get tears to spend here, so it burns my throat and makes me want to hurt you and all who are like you, so numb to everything, so immune. All I have is the sun and soft cooing of pigeons and a longing to know who to touch, how to shout, to get back in, among the breathing.

LOST AND FOUND

Catherine Jones

Walking through the side streets of this city, I have seen: 123 gloves placed carefully on railings or walls, waiting for their other halves; 49 individual lost shoes, not counting those strung over trees or wires outside houses; 30 coats hung up on a bush or a fence; 23 mobile phones on the floor (of which 12 smashed); 16 broken and abandoned umbrellas; 7 children's stuffed toys, unloved; 4 lost wallets; 3 abandoned children's scooters; 1 bunch of keys; and a prosthetic leg which someone must be missing. But why would you go back for what you've left behind when this city seems so hostile? Locks are changed, new phones and umbrellas bought. Life goes on. 123 lonely gloves linger in cupboards and drawers.

DANCE WHERE NO ONE WATCHES

Cath Holland

We met on the final warm night of the year in a bar near enough empty, and well away from the hipster hangouts. The place had sticky carpets and a DJ playing 1990s songs from his iPod. A low-lying cloud wrung itself dry and speckled the windows as you bought me wine. Happy hour had been and gone yet the barman chucked a third of a bottle into a pint glass, plonked it on the bar and said 'Three Fifty'. There was no please, no thank you but I sipped my drink and enjoyed the quiet buzz.

We stepped outside. Taxis honked horns and rubber tyres rolled as they drove past, sound-tracking the tongues of moist light licking the side street. I wondered what the flat grey flags tasted like, bleached filament-white by headlights. The drama of this side of town was a film set, the pavement patterned with flattened rounds of chewing gum, urban glitter. I'd never danced before, not properly, but the wet varnished the ground into a dance floor, just for us. You took the lead. My joints oiled, belly drawn in, spine straight and chin high and happy, I learned fast, heels clicking in a percussive shuffle. I didn't mind when the rain came back later, the sly type that soaks right through. The soft punch and plop of each raindrop brightened my face, and washed the sweat from my brow. It darkened my hair and thickened my eyelashes, made my dress cling.

We drew out the hours, stretched the minutes and seconds every which way and that, to make them last. I asked if you were coming back here again. You smiled 'of course!' and meant it too, for the seconds it took to say. But you knew, I think, we can't recreate perfect things. Best to keep them safe instead, well thumbed by time, soft around the edges.

There's been plenty of delicious firsts since, mind, pushing the pleasure buttons one by one. And I have a good man these days, dependable, and mine. Even now though, when it's a mild autumn or winter is late, maybe, and rain mizzles down after dark, I re-waltz the exact same dance floor. When the stars go blurry and drunk, I twirl in a tangle of raindrops stretched into fine strings. Feel your hand on my back and another settled at my waist holding me tight, and right. The world around me is a jukebox, there's wine in every ale house to make my insides glow. We'll always have rain here in the city, thank God. And we'll always feel the push and the pull, and a sharp tug to the heart, at each dark and hidden corner.

CAREFUL WHERE YOU TREAD

Rosamund Davies

Around that corner, many years ago, a little girl trailed behind her mother, hopping from one paving stone to the next, taking care not to tread in between them onto the cracks, because she knew that, if she did, the bears would jump out and get her.

'Come on,' her mother said, 'walk normally.'

'I can't,' said the little girl, 'if I do, the bears will get me.'

Her mother laughed. 'Well, hop a bit faster!' she said.

The little girl took no notice, but carried on hopping and skipping at exactly the same pace. They passed on by.

Today, at this moment, a little girl comes round the corner, trailing behind her mother, hopping from one paving stone to the next, taking care not to tread in between them onto the cracks, because she knows that, if she does, the bears will jump out and get her.

'Come on,' her mother says, 'walk normally.'

'I can't,' says the little girl, 'if I do, the bears will get me.'

'Don't be silly,' says her mother. 'Hurry up!'

The little girl takes no notice, but carries on hopping and skipping at exactly the same pace. They pass on by.

Under the paving stones the bears wait, still hoping that one day they'll get their chance.

HOLE IN THE WALL

Ash Lim

The best food is often found in alleys at night, in dimly lit side streets with only a few flickering signboards to light the way. A laughing couple passes you by, raindrops bouncing off their umbrella while your shoes slosh through deep puddles. You battle through the blistering wind as you pick up the faint scent of tempting, welcoming food carried on it. You desperately hope for something hot, something that would scald your tongue and bubble in your gut like a boiling pot of soup but will wrap your body in enough warmth to carry you through the rest of the night.

So, you keep going.

You know you're there when your senses are violently assaulted. Not just by the smells of the dishes themselves, but by the deafening noise of the patrons inside the small, hidden restaurant. Groups, couples, and the occasional solo eater all squeezed into a hole in the wall, beer bottles clinking against each other as office workers celebrate the end of a long day, roars of the only chef as he sends out plates and plates of piping hot food.

You squeeze in, managing to fit yourself into one of the corners of the restaurant. A sparse menu printed on a sheet of laminated paper is thrust in front of you; the waiter is already waiting for your order. He knows you don't need the menu, because every single person who comes here ignores the menu. You're no different, and you place your order with a quick grin: the chef's special for one, please.

While you wait, you twiddle your thumbs and look around you, living, breathing, and just taking it all in. Some faded posters are plastered on the walls, and possibly a few decades ago you would be able to tell whether it was an advertisement for the bakery down the street or a photograph of a famous rock band. You watch the waiters bustle about, steaming bowls and hot plates teetering in their skilled hands as they rush to keep up with the restaurant's flow. Whatever music there is playing in the background has long been drowned out by the everyday slap of sneakers against the floor, and the reverb of metal utensils hitting against each other as they are gathered up.

You know it has arrived before you even see it laid on the table before you. You know that the one bowl of soup that just left the kitchen is going to find its way to you; true to your instincts, the waiter weaves his way around the crowded tables to bestow his charity upon you.

When it hits the table, you bear witness to a new world through billowing clouds of fragrant steam. With a trembling hand you carefully dip your spoon into the rich broth and lift it to your mouth to taste.

Was it worth the exhausting trek through a rainy night? Absolutely.

PASSAGE

Jess Kilby

Laneways are for hidden things. For hiding things. When you grow weary of the city step into the shadow of a narrow lane and you will become invisible, I promise you. The sunlight will lose sight of your face, for just a moment, and you will slip through.

You are in here now. In the silence, and the stillness. Don't sit down though, on that milk crate or that gummy doorstep. Keep moving. But slowly, slowly. Because laneways are also for finding things. You might think I'm being metaphorical, and there's that too. But I mean real things. A Coke can crushed into the shape of a heart. A rose petal floating on an iridescent puddle. A cigarette lighter that still has some spark. If you are looking-but-not-looking you might find other things as well – a discarded lotto ticket, the glossy feather of an unfamiliar bird. Look up: ballet shoes dangling from the power lines.

Certain things will seem too insignificant to matter, as if their presence is to be expected. Surely every laneway in this city is strewn with old bolts and rusted nails, with bottle caps and broken glass? The glass pops and crunches underfoot, one step closer to becoming glitter. This city is paved in glitter.

The longer you linger, the more you will discover. Linger long enough and you will become invisible even to yourself. What will you discover then? A play of colour between the graffiti and the rubbish bins? A luminous alchemy of sunwashed stone and shadowed brick? You might perceive patterns in the cracked concrete, or see for the first time the weeds and wildflowers at the edge of everything.

Metal washers, plastic straws, a curl of orange twine. A leather glove, a pink ribbon tied around a drainage pipe.

You will put some things in your pocket; you will leave other things behind. Most things you will leave behind. But you will take those things with you, too. And here I am being metaphorical, and also not. For once you have seen a rose petal drifting in an oily puddle – I mean have really *seen* it; have watched the clouds float by until your petal has sailed a thousand skies; have learned to tell the tides from the slightest stirring of a breeze – once you have known these things, they belong to you. And you belong to them. Even as you slip from shadow once more into light, as you cross the busy intersection and are swallowed up by spectacle, you remain one with all that is hidden – and all that is waiting to be found.

TECH DOWN

Nic Vine

Feet hurt too much walking explore off beaten track solo adventure internet safety net good idea phone died no idea where I am shops shut no-one around city side streets all look the same why is there no-one now it's raining I'll have to walk perhaps that street crash hello tarmac why am I lying under a bicycle can you help me loud swearing man bicycle gone limp round the corner rain comes harder into archway sink to floor rub hands and knees can't stay here must be that way left and right and left and right still no clues here's a square giant trees sheltered benches sit and rest…doze…sleep…jerk awake shiver cold up again and on repurposed warehouses tall dark building sites blocks of flats all secure all quiet pressing a button too weird I wouldn't answer me why no phone boxes why no street maps bloody internet bloody faulty charger leg hurts really not funny church for sanctuary imposing oak doors firmly locked I'd pay tithe by plastic nearby doorway here's plastic and cardboard need sleep make a bed ow here's a body not warm not good why is there no-one stumble on get help remember church tower faceless streets streaming wet finally bar open empty barman looks reach for wallet no wallet where wallet tarmac wallet bloody bloody cyclist ask help ask police church body no understand shout louder wild eyed hello street door slam sob gasp street bucks and turns buildings leer down threaten why is this happening what did I take why is this happening what did I take what did I TAKE breathe breathe breathe must rest must sleep mustn't sleep not here stand up lean on wall stagger on endless side streets no life here's a square same square going in circles to the square so hungry smell food check bin soggy bun red sauce try ahead not left not right leg hurt arm hurt head swim keep going window light door push warmth greeting supporting arm bench rest...soup bread tea...camp bed shoes off blanket...salvation...sleep.

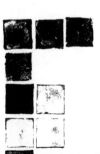

SQUARES
AND
PARKS

SIC TRANSIT GLORIA MUNDI

Cathy Lennon

They made me out of bronze. There is a permanence to bronze, you know. The rain – there's a lot of rain – and the pigeons are just irritations that do nothing to destroy my essential solidity. Day and night I like to survey the square from my plinth. My right arm is slung across my waist and my left juts out at an angle, which, I am sorry to say, proves something of a temptation to the nocturnal passers-by. Training shoes have been strung over it, and umbrellas hung. Every September I am guaranteed a traffic cone for a hat. One night, a woman with a ring through her nose and magenta coils of hair covered me in yarn. It made the city news.

There is a peculiar man who comes from time to time and stands opposite me. He is dressed like me and covered with paint. He strikes the same pose and when the children approach, he stays very still. Even when they poke him. But he disappears in the late afternoon and sometimes I don't see him again for weeks. Another man comes most days and unpacks a trolley. He pours sand onto a board at my feet and with great care and skill he makes a sculpture of a sleeping dog. I have always loved dogs. If I could speak I would tell the sculptor that he should do it in bronze, because bronze is permanent. The sculptor has eyes as blank as mine. I am not sure he understands what permanent means.

Just lately people with clipboards have come. They are conducting a poll, they say. Some of the people they approach just ignore them but others nod their heads vigorously and sign the petition. 'It's about time,' they say. 'Not a single woman,' they say. 'Imperialist,' they say. I can't speak, of course. I just stare out across the square. They will be gone eventually. But I am made out of bronze and I am permanent.

TRUING THE SQUARE

Dave Murray

She invites him to sit in her favourite park, in the middle of the city square, on the bench with the dedication to a marriage of thirty-two years, the one with a faint canopy of foliage so you can just feel the rain, hoping he will return to this place after she has left.

He takes her to his favourite coffee shop, the one that lets you choose the origin of the beans, sitting in the window where you can discern the reflections when the light is just right, imprinting a virtual image of the two of them sitting side by side that he will later recall.

She shows him the bakery to which she has walked every week, knowing that once he has tasted their apricot tart he will return at least occasionally (perhaps one day they will ask him how he found the shop and he will start by saying *my friend used to*).

He tells her to look up at the exquisite markings in the brickwork on the side of the old hotel, because *only by looking up do we see the real city*, a phrase that he hopes she will remember in every city that she passes through in the future.

She leads him down an alleyway, through a graffiti sprayed door and into a small room with a serving hatch that leads onto a kitchen where she hands over a note in exchange for a paper bag containing small, white parcels of seafood, knowing he could never find it again.

In the bar on the corner of the square, he plays a jukebox for the first time in ten years, paying for one song from the album she has just told him is her favourite, in the hope that she will remember him every time she hears the song in another city.

They walk together, hand in hand, to the corner of the square where office workers wait patiently for the green man. They kiss in the knowledge that they are seen, in the knowledge that they have left a memory in this square.

SPIDER GOES TO THE PARK

Melaina Barnes

Imagine I am spider. Not an absurd insect-human, not a fantasy monster robot imitation. Just spider.

Small, work-a-day thing. Spider of wing mirrors, railings, tunnels and threads.

I crawl. I search for blades of grass. I need them, yes I do.

Cracks of green in broken streets. Cobbles, concrete, can't resist when stems insist and grow.

They're what I want. But more than that, an open space, full of green, where I can dream.

Noisy dogs. Unhappy whines and barks break hearts as they ask to be let out. They can't run, not now, not down the streets where I crawl on hydraulic legs.

Bee wings, o rapidity, o joy to follow. I am too slow, too slow. They know the way to go. Try to guess the path. Pneumatic push in my control to find the point where vistas open up.

The city's streets keep things in place, no roundabouts crawl off. I want the point where they give up. Where I can run, jump, move. Full of fluidity. Before the death curl that will come in its own time.

Compressed crawl, slowing now. Feet drag in rain. And there it is. A gap, a path of broken stones. I follow. I hope.

And here I am. Space full of breeze. Green leaves, green earth. Clover to climb. All legs tremble, heart beats fast.

Dew at dawn. Every droplet vibrates. Every droplet sings. And the song draws from deep earth the knowledge of creatures who went to sleep. Now spider is the one who knows.

Imagine I am spider.

SURVIVOR

Rachael McGill

I was so excited when they told us the conditions were right to visit the old city. Some people come the whole way and have to make do with the Island Parks and the overpriced souvenir shops because the weather's too bad for the dive. This trip to the motherland had used up all my savings: it was my only chance. We transferred from our aerial pod to a diving pod through a translucent tunnel, so we weren't exposed to the air (poisonous, they said), but I heard the wind whistling, felt the diving pod tilt with the movement of the sea. The water was so opaque it looked black. I ached to touch it.

The sea was murky – we wouldn't have seen a thing without the laser beams and the virtual host directing us where to look. A glass and metal structure loomed into view, covered in green and brown blotches. The host said 'your wrist screens show an image of this building as it originally appeared. The organic material that now covers it is sea life; native algae and crustaceans.'

I preferred the building as it looked now, fascinating textures all over it. The image was just a taller version of the constructions I was used to.

'This building stood at the head of a grand square in the centre of this city,' said the host, 'which was the capital of the nation that existed when this land was above the sea. It was one of the richest cities on earth.'

'Can we get out and look for treasure?' someone joked. We'd all heard the fairy stories.

The host didn't catch the humour, or chose to ignore it. 'The wealth of cities like this was like our wealth,' it said, 'principally virtual, rather than material. This was a civilisation almost as advanced as our own.'

Something glinted at the edge of my vision. I looked out of the window into an unblinking grey eye. Around the eye was scaly skin. I'd seen images of fish, but this was different. I'd always thought non-human creatures were like robots, but they were more like people than I'd imagined. The fish seemed to be having thoughts I couldn't understand, about me. I wanted to apologise to it, on behalf of my ancestors, who'd left its ancestors behind on a poisonous planet with cataclysmic weather. Of course it wasn't really the fish I pitied, but the long ago people without savings to spend on interplanetary travel, who hadn't been able to escape.

They'd warned us about thoughts like this before we entered the mother planet's atmosphere – emotional reactions to all the different colours here, feelings of loss, survivor guilt. We were supposed to take a calming pill. I fingered one out from the pocket in my belt. The fish floated, level with my face. 'Should I take this?' I whispered. It flicked its silvery tail and disappeared.

IN THE PARK, MAN WITH THE GUITAR

Kam Rehal

There he is, man, just out there.

So far, with nothing, just all alone – yeah sure all those others are there too, cameras, smiles, clicks, shuffles, glancing back, letting it affect them like the softest ripple touch, hands – but for him it's just the deepest, coldest time. It's just him. He's not actually reaching them the way he needs it. Listen:

How can he keep on like this?

It's desperate, spectacular, a spectacle, useless – shifting, *clicks,* small stroller wheels, *clicks,* children patter, waves, travellers get their bearings, soft claps –

'. . . .|||||.,||||.,.||||...|.,|||,.|.,||.,|||. . . .'

He can't, can't stop it, moving further out toward them, just no use.

'. . . .||||..,|||..||||..,||.,.|.,||||||. . . .'

It's not what they register, he can't get it all, any of it, to them.

He'll be here again tomorrow.

ON WHOSE BENCH ARE YOU SITTING?

Jane Roberts

Sit on the bench in the square for long enough and you will hear the pigeons speak to you. You will not understand them at first, and that will be most frustrating for them. But speak they will, regardless of your auditory deficiencies.

The pigeons will tell you about the woman on whose bench you are sitting. It is their favourite story to tell, even as they defecate on her brass memorial plaque – inscribed in a font the deceased would never have chosen.

The pigeons will tell you about a man who once released a pair of exotic yellow birds into the shaded sanctuary of the square after the passing of his lover, the woman on whose bench you are sitting. They will admit that they were envious of those summer season feathers, these pigeons that are dressed for eternity in drab winter greys.

The day the woman found out she had just months to live, she sat in the square and listened to the pigeons and considered the abyss before her: the cracks in the tarmac of the path, sucked dry by the invisible tree roots on either side; the grass that was soil brown bare – beneath a special tree with initials carved deep with love into its trunk – planted with more footprints of paramours than blades of grass. The pigeons will tell you these amorous carvings were made by the man who set birds free – and the woman on whose bench you are sitting.

There are glimpses of windows through the canopy of the trees – offices, homes. Blinds pulled half down as if there is a tax on nosiness. The pigeons know what lies behind these blinds. The woman often looked up and wondered about the secrets behind the blinds; her viewpoint incomplete as she waited for lunch with her lover on the bench on which you are sitting.

The pigeons knew her as the woman who fed them pieces of her lunchtime sandwich each day, as she sat on a bench picked at random – that then became her bench. The bench on which she was sitting when she met the man; although his choice of bench was not random. The bench on which you are sitting.

The pigeons – if you choose to listen – will tell you that the woman who once sat on this bench could be you.

Close your eyes and listen to the pigeons.

HAPPY NEW YEAR

Maja Bodenstein

It's the fifth day of Lunar New Year; a dusting of snow rests on the red lanterns strung across the market square. I'm queuing at a bun stall when a voice calls out my full name. I turn around and see my childhood friend barrel her way through the crowd.

We haven't seen each other for over twenty years, and yet I know her immediately. She's dressed in a beautiful coat, a slim-fit, accentuating her long lines. She hasn't grown up beautiful, as everyone expected; but she holds herself with a grace and self-possession that strikes me as rarer than beauty.

'What a coincidence,' she laughs.

'Small world,' I bring out.

We smile, shifting our feet to stave off the cold. The man in front of me grabs his order; I'm next.

'My treat. For old times' sake,' she says, rummaging in her handbag for change; it's a Louis Vuitton. I self-consciously rub my shirt collar. It's a good brand, favoured by golfers, but I look shabby beside her.

The buns are soft and fluffy; I take a bite. A gust of steam escapes, washing me in memory.

We grew up in a village, in a strange time with little food, and few adults. Our mothers had been sent north; nobody knew where her father was. We were both raised by loving grandparents, who fed us rice and made do with coarse grains. There had been hopes linking the two of us, but when her father returned, he moved the whole family abroad.

We eat and trade small talk that reveals nothing but the most superficial aspects of our lives. She is married, no children; I'm divorced. She makes appropriate noises of sympathy. I wonder what her life has been like, to shape her into this slightly-too-formal individual, that our speech should be made up of clichés.

Perhaps she wonders, too. She pauses, mid-sentence, and asks: 'Do you remember the hawthorn tree in the yard?'

I do. As children, nothing thrilled us more than watching those red buds ripen, holding the promise of candied fruits. Later, it was the site of our first kiss; a hurried brush of the lips, more curiosity than desire.

'I wonder if that tree is still there.'

'You've not been back? The old plots are all gone. It's a shopping mall now.'

'Figures. My father never wanted to go back. I guess I'm following in his footsteps; more than he knew.'

There's a hint of bitterness at the side of her mouth. Before I can decipher it, she smiles with renewed brightness. I understand; our meeting is over.

'Good to see you. Really, what a coincidence.'

'Yes, truly.'

We shake hands – her fingertips briefly brush my wrist, strangely warm in the cold – and I steel myself to rejoin the faceless crowd. I take a step.

'Hey, wait,' she suddenly says.

I turn back. She opens her mouth, thinks better of it, and smiles. 'Happy new year.'

'Happy new year,' I reply, and walk away.

HUMANS OF

Belinda Huang

When my boyfriend and I first started dating, the public park was where we spent our time together. In the bloom of a first relationship we lay underneath trees with our legs entwined, kissing desperately while toddlers trampled the tulip displays nearby.

One Friday, we were kissing on a park bench when a man stopped and asked to take our photo. For his credentials, he gave us a business card for a locally popular website. He said he had passed by our bench fifteen minutes earlier to photograph someone else, and on his return noticed that we were still kissing in the same position. Could he take our picture?

This photographer's arrival was a sign that our very new relationship was meant to be. While he set up his tripod and camera, the man asked, why do you like kissing so much? My boyfriend, the philosopher, started his response with Spinoza and the universal substance of which we are all a part. Kissing, he said, is how we repair the damage done by separating ourselves from each other. I buried my face in his shoulder, feeling his arm move as he gesticulated.

Months later, the picture appeared online. You can see the arm of his denim jacket around my shoulder, pulling me closer. His hair is dark and perfect, and his eyes are closed as our lips come close to meeting. My hair is tied up in a loose bun, and I'm wearing my purple rain jacket. You can't see my face at all.